Imant Raminsh
Of Mothers and Children

Five Irish Lyrics
for Soprano and Piano

DISTRIBUTED BY

CORPORATION
7777 W. BLUEMOUND RD. P.O. BOX 13819 MILWAUKEE, WI 53213

www.boosey.com
www.halleonard.com

OF MOTHERS AND CHILDREN
(Five Irish Lyrics for Soprano Voice and Piano)

The relationship between mother and child is something uniquely intimate, mystical, and profound. In the cycle *Of Mothers and Children* (1993), this relationship is explored through the exquisite evocative lyrical poetry of five Irish poets.

Song 1, *The Woman with Child,* offers a secret insight into the earliest stage of this connection. The text is set somewhat freely beginning with a quasi-recitative of very narrow range. Progressively the melodic line opens up like a flower bud opening to the sun. Song 2, *Lullaby of the Woman of the Mountain,* is the first of several lullabies. Its magical poetic image inspires rapturous musical expression. The verse form of the text is echoed in the music. Song 3, *A Cradle Song,* set in a regular 6/8 rhythm, has more of a rocking feel than Song 2. Song 4, *Fairy Nurse,* has a delicate dance-like quality and features a flowing sixteenth-note accompaniment supporting a fairly angular melodic line. Song 5, *A Little Boy in the Morning,* is tinged with melancholy and suggests the deepest tragedy – the loss of a child.

– Imant Raminsh

1. THE WOMAN WITH CHILD

How I am held within a tranquil shell,
As if I too were close within a womb,
I too enfolded as I fold the child.

As the tight bud enwraps the pleated leaf,
The blossom furled like an enfolded fan,
So life enfold me as I fold my flower.

As water lies within a lovely bowl,
I lie within my life, and life again
Lies folded fast with my living cell.

The apple waxes at the blossom's root,
And like the moon I mellow to the round
Full circle of my being, till I too

Am ripe with living and my fruit is grown.
Then break the shell of life. We shall be born,
My child and I, together, to the sun.

— Freda Laughton*

2. LULLABY OF THE WOMAN OF THE MOUNTAIN

O little head of Gold! O candle of my house!
Thou wilt guide all who travel this country.

Be quiet, O house! And O little grey mice
Stay at home tonight in your hidden lairs!

O moths on the window, fold your wings!
Stay at home tonight, O little black chafers!

O plover and O curlew, over my house do not travel!
Speak not, O barnacle-goose, going over the mountain here!

O creatures of the mountain, that wake so early
Stir not to-night till the sun whitens over you.

— Padraic Pearce
translated by Thomas MacDonagh

3. A CRADLE SONG

O, men from the fields!
Come gently within.
Tread softly, softly,
O! men coming in.

Mavourneen is going
From me and from you
Where Mary will fold him
With mantle of blue!

From reek of the smoke
And cold of the floor,
And the peering of things
Across the half-door.

O men from the fields!
Soft, softly come through!
Mary puts round him
Her mantle of blue.
— *Padraic Colum*

4. FAIRY NURSE

Sweet babe! A golden cradle holds thee,
And soft the snow-white fleece enfold thee;
In airy bower I'll watch thy sleeping.
Where branchy trees to the breeze are sweeping.
Shuheen, sho, lulo, lo!

When mothers languish broken-hearted,
When young wives are from husbands parted,
Ah! Little think the keeners lonely,
They weep some time-worn fairy only.
Shuheen, sho, lulo, lo!

Within our magic halls of brightness
Trips many a foot of snowy whiteness;
Stolen maidens, queens of fairy —
And kings and chiefs a slaugh-shee airy.
Shuheen, sho, lulo, lo!

Rest thee babe! I love thee dearly,
And as thy mortal mother nearly;
Ours is the swiftest steed and proudest,
That moves where the tramps of the host is loudest.
Shuheen, sho, lulo, lo!

Rest thee babe! For soon thy slumbers
Shall flee at the magic koelshie's numbers;
In airy bower I'll watch thy sleeping.
Where branchy trees to the breeze are sweeping.
Shuheen, sho, lulo, lo!
— *Edward Walsh*

5. A LITTLE BOY IN THE MORNING

He will not come, and still I wait.
He whistles at another gate
Where angels listen. Ah, I know
He will not come, yet if I go
How shall I know he did not pass
Barefooted in the flowery grass?

The moon leans on one silver horn
Above the silhouettes of morn,
And from their nest sills finches whistle
Or stooping pluck the downy thistle.
How is the morn so gay and fair
Without his whistling in its air?

The world is calling, I must go.
How shall I know he did not pass
Barefooted in the shining grass?
— *Francis Ledwidge*

* The publisher has used its best efforts to clear any copyrighted text that might be included in this work with the relevant owners and to print suitable acknowledgements. If any right owner has not been consulted or an acknowledgement omitted, the publisher offers its apology and will rectify the situation following formal notification.

OF MOTHERS AND CHILDREN
(Five Irish Lyrics for Soprano & Piano)
1. The Woman with Child

Words by
Freda Laughton*

Music by
Imant Raminsh

*The publisher has used its best efforts to clear any copyrighted text that might be included in this work with the relevant owners and to print suitable acknowledgments. If any right owner has not been consulted or an acknowledgment omitted, the publisher offers its apology and will rectify the situation following formal notification.

rit.　*a tempo*

I ___ too en-fold-ed _ as I fold _ the child. _____

As the tight _ bud, _____ as _ the tight _ bud en - wraps the pleat-ed leaf, the

blos-som furled like an en - fold-ed fan. _ So _ life en-fold me _ as I fold my flower.

meno mosso

Tempo Iº

As wa-ter lies, as wa-ter lies _ with - in a love - ly bowl, ___

The ap-ple wax-es at the blos-som's root, And like the moon I mel-low to the round full

cir-cle of my be-ing, till I too am ripe with liv-ing, with liv-ing, I too am ripe with

liv-ing, with liv-ing, I too am ripe with liv-ing, with liv-ing, with liv-ing, and my

fruit, my fruit is grown, my fruit is grown.

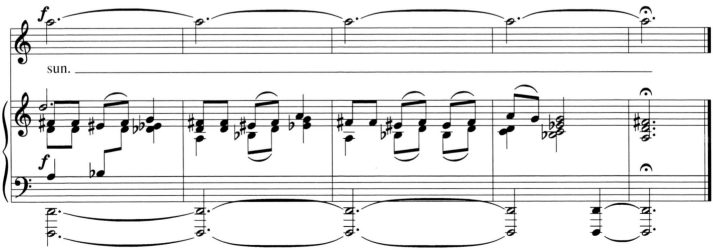

2. Lullaby of the Woman of the Mountain

Padraic Pearce
translated by
Thomas MacDonagh

coun - try. Be qui - et, O house! And O lit-tle grey

mice _____ Stay _ at home to - night _

_____ in _ your hid - den lairs! Stay at home to - night _____ in _ your hid - den, hid - den

pochiss. rit.

moun-tain, the moun-tain, the moun-tain here!

pochiss. rit.

poco a poco dim. . . .

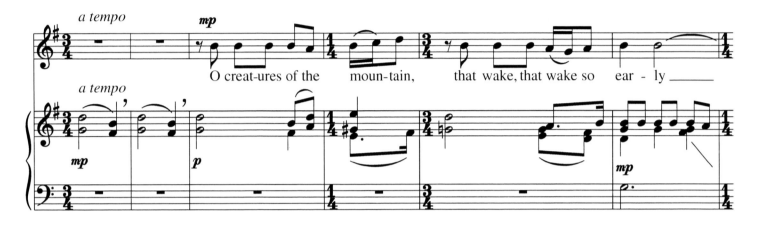

a tempo

O creat-ures of the moun-tain, that wake, that wake so ear - ly ___

Stir ___ not to-night ___ till ___ the sun whit-ens oèr you,

più f

Stir ___ not to-night ___ till ___ the sun ___ whit-ens oèr you. ___

3. A Cradle Song

Words by
Padraic Colum

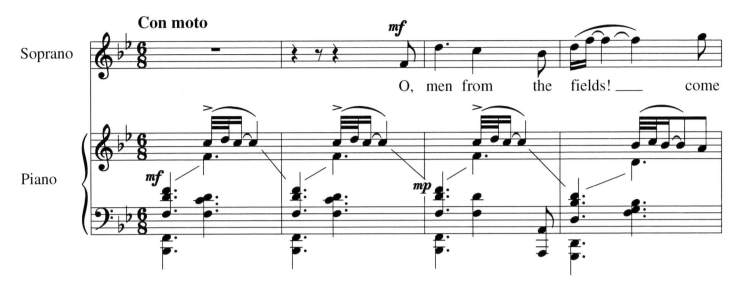

O, men from the fields! ___ come

gen-tly, gen-tly with-in. ___ Tread soft - ly, soft-ly. ___ O! men com-ing

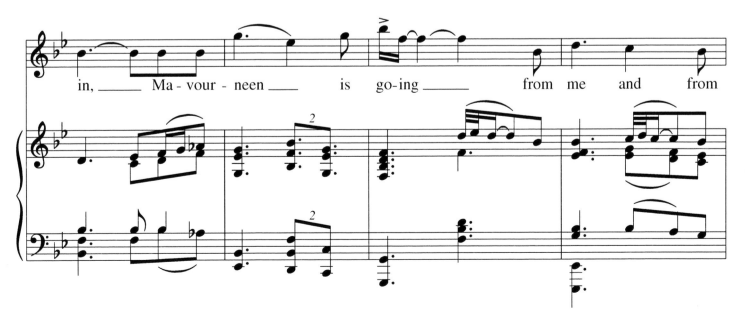

in, ___ Ma - vour - neen ___ is go-ing ___ from me and from

M-051-93383-9

you ____ Where Ma - ry will fold him ____ with man - tle ____ of

blue! _____ From reek of the

smoke ____ and cold, cold of the floor, And the peer - ing of

things ____ A - cross the half - door. ___ O men from the

fields! _____ soft, soft - ly come through! _____ Ma - ry puts

round him ____ her man - tle ___ of blue. _____ O man - tle,

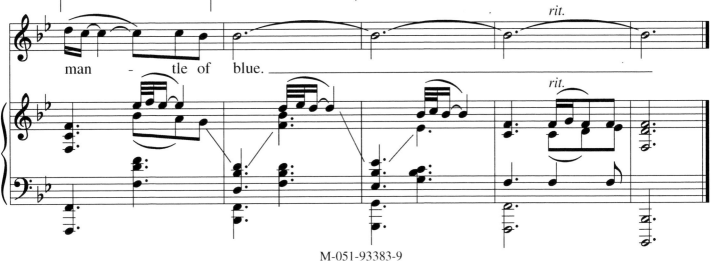

man - tle of blue. _____

4. Fairy Nurse

Words by
Edward Walsh

watch thy sleep - ing. _ Where branch - y trees to the

breeze are sweep - ing. _ Shu - heen, sho, lu - lo, lo!

rit. *a tempo*

Shu - heen, sho, _ lu - lo, lo, _ lo! _

When moth - ers lan - guish

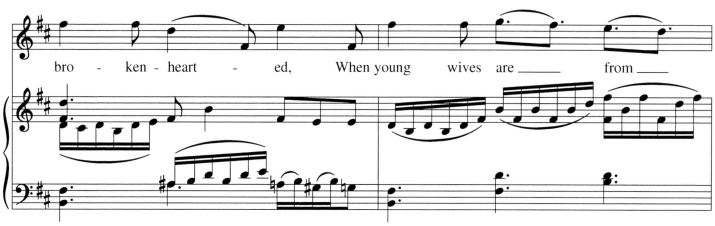

bro - ken - heart - ed, When young wives are _____ from _____

hus - bands part - ed, _____ Ah! lit - tle think the

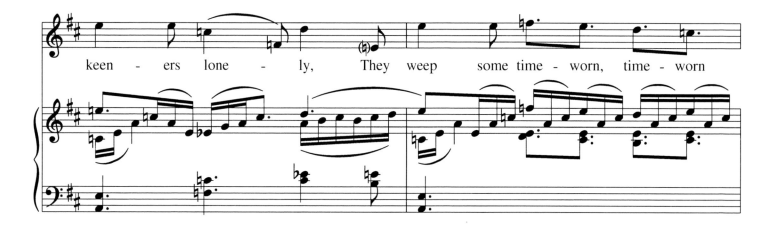

keen - ers lone - ly, They weep some time - worn, time - worn

fai - ry on - ly. Shu - heen, _ sho, shu - heen, _ sho, lu -

lo, _____ lu - lo, _____ lu - lo, lu - lo, lo, lo. With-

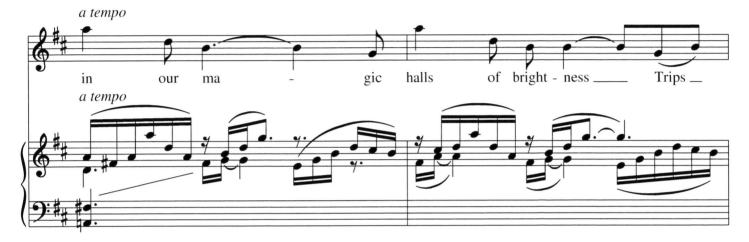

in our ma - gic halls of bright - ness _____ Trips _

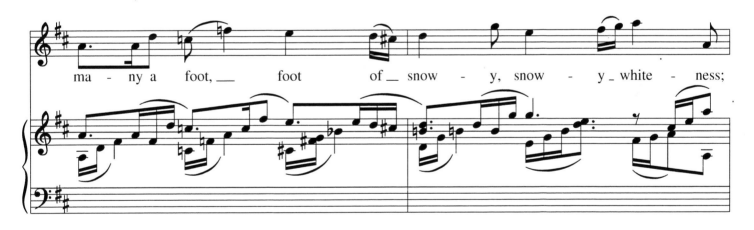

ma - ny a foot, _____ foot of _ snow - y, snow - y _ white - ness;

Sto - len mai - dens, _____ queens of fai - ry _ And _

kings and chiefs _____ a slaugh - shee air - y.

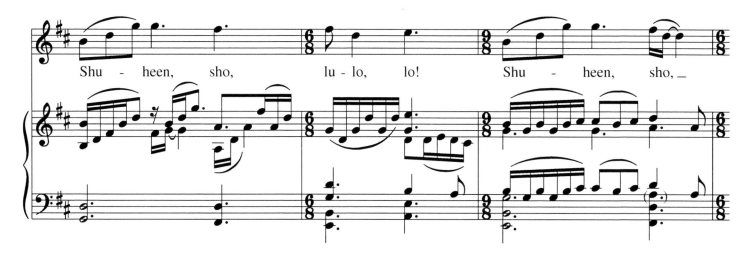

Shu - heen, sho, lu - lo, lo! Shu - heen, sho, _

lu - lo, lo, lu - lo, lo, lu - lo, lo. _____

rit.

Molto tranquillo

Rest thee babe! I love thee

dear - ly, rest _ thee _ babe! _ I love thee dear - ly, And as thy mor-tal moth - er _

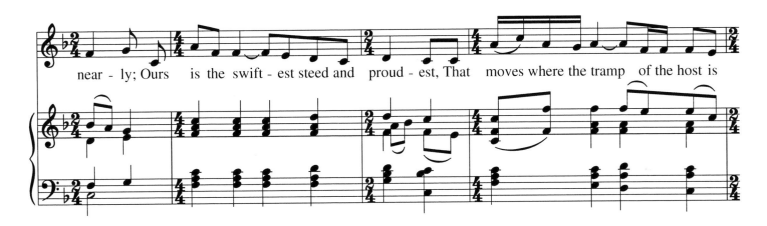

near - ly; Ours is the swift - est steed and proud - est, That moves where the tramp of the host is

loud - est. Shu - heen, _ sho - lu - lo, Shu - heen, _ sho - lu - lo,

allargando

lo, shu - heen, _ sho - lu - lo, lo! _____
allargando

Tempo I

Rest thee babe! _____ for _ soon thy slum - bers _____ Shall_

flee, shall flee at the mag - ic, _ mag - ic koel - shie's num-bers; In

air - y bo - wer _____ I'll watch thy sleep - ing. _ Where_

branch - y trees to the breeze are sweep - ing. _____

Shu - heen, sho, lu - lo, lo, Shu - heen, sho, _

lu - lo, lo, lu - lo, lo,

Shu - heen, sho, ___ lu - lo, lu - lo, lo, lo! _____

5. A Little Boy in the Morning

Words by
Francis Ledwidge

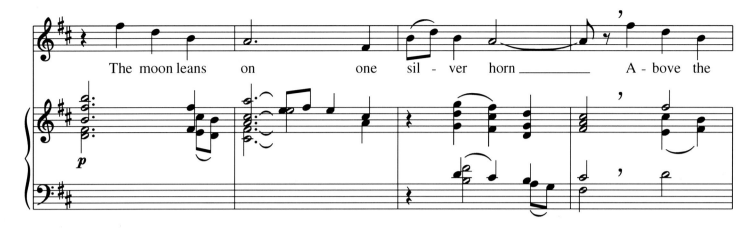

The moon leans on one sil-ver horn _____ A-bove the

sil - hou-ettes of morn, And from their nest sills fin - ches

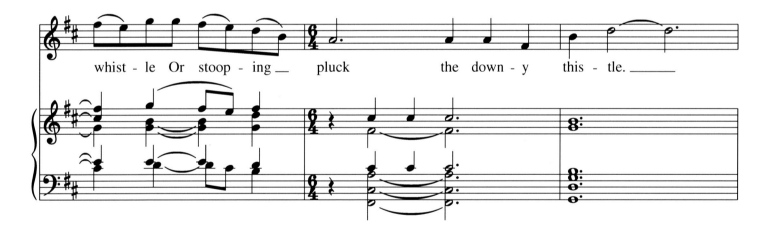

whist - le Or stoop-ing __ pluck the down-y this-tle. _____

How is the morn so gay and fair _____ With-out his __ whist-ling in the

air? The world is call - ing, the world is

call - ing, I __ must go.

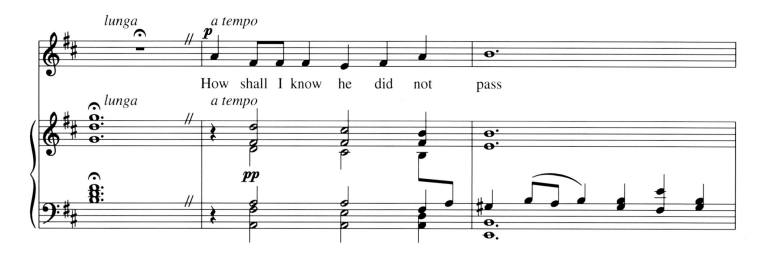

lunga *a tempo*

How shall I know he did not pass

Bare - foot-ed in the shin - ing grass? _____

 August 1993